Maths for the More Able – A Challenge a Week

YEAR 2

Dr Alan Stoker

Introduction

This series of six photocopiable books provides additional challenge for more able children. The materials enable you to meet the needs of able mathematicians without developing completely separate topics.

For users of the NNS
Maths For the More Able can be integrated easily into whatever maths material you use if you are following the NNS. The contents list on the inside front cover gives the appropriate reference to the NNS pages. The book contains stimulating challenges to enhance the range of children's mathematical experience.

You can use this book to:
- provide alternative, and more demanding, tasks for more able children during the group work phase of the daily maths lesson;
- provide more challenging homework tasks for the more able mathematicians in your class;
- broaden the range of mathematical experience for a range of children.

Many of the tasks in this book are of an investigative or puzzle-solving variety. In addition to mathematical knowledge, some logical thinking will often be required. The children should enjoy the level of challenge the activities provide, and

also the opportunity to choose their own ways of working. This is fundamental to development in mathematics, and you should therefore allow children to decide what aids they will use to help them solve the problems. More able children are often comfortable with abstract tasks, but most of them will at some stage want to use practical apparatus, and this should be allowed.

For users of the Folens Maths Programme
The teacher's pages are correlated to specific lessons in the FMP. You can therefore substitute for your able pupils the activity in this book for the one indicated for that day in the FMP.

The pupil sheets
Photocopiable activity sheets (**AS**) for the children to work on are provided for the lessons and can be used to support group work. It is assumed that all the children will take part in the whole-class introduction to the lesson before tackling the task from this book. Note that Week 7 in each term is set aside for assessment and review.

The teacher notes will guide you in introducing the tasks to the children and in effective ways of working, as well as providing the solutions. These notes will help you to support children appropriately as they work.

Counting and properties of numbers

Learning objectives

◆ Count in steps of 2, 4 and 5.
◆ Begin to recognise familiar multiples.

Resources

AS 'Strange dice'
Counters

Teacher's notes

In this activity children move round a track which has 60 spaces from start to finish. Children are not told that there are 60 spaces. (The first square after the start counts as 'one'; ensure that the children understand this, and that they don't count the start square.)

In the first part children work out multiples of four and count on. After three throws they have to calculate how many fours are needed to land exactly on the finish square.

The first throw is 4 x 4 = 16; the second throw is 2 x 4 = 8; the third throw is 3 x 4 = 12.
The total number of squares moved = 16 + 8 + 12 = 36.
There are 24 spaces to reach the finish. This requires a throw of **6 fours**.

In the second part children work out multiples of five and count on. After two throws they have to calculate how many fives are needed to land exactly on the finish square.
First throw is 5 fives = 25; The second throw is 2 fives = 10.
The total number of spaces moved = 25 + 10 = 35. There are 25 spaces to reach the finish.
This requires a throw of **5 fives**.

In the final part children use multiples of two to create their own problem.

Strange dice

You are using two strange dice. They throw only fours. You are going round the track using these strange dice.

- Your first throw is 4 fours. Work out this number. Count on from the start.
- Your next throw is 2 fours. Work out this number and count on.
- Your next throw is 3 fours. Work out this number and count on.

How many fours do you need to throw to land exactly on the finish square?

- You now use another two dice that throw only fives. Go from the start.
- These are your throws: first throw 5 fives; second throw 2 fives.

How many fives do you need to land exactly on the finish?

Make up your own problem with two dice that throw only twos.

start finish

Place value and addition

Learning objectives

◆ Recognise the relationship between digits in a two-digit number and combine numbers to make a two-digit number.

Resources

AS 'What number am I?'

Teacher's notes

This problem-solving activity is in the form of number stories.

There are four tasks. In each part children must use the clues provided to find the number.

Task one:
From the first clue, the number is one of these 3 **4** 5 6 7 8 9.

From the second clue, to make 25 from each of the four numbers requires additions:
9 + 16 , 12 + 13 , 21 + **4** , 23 + 2.

The only number fitting both clues is **4**. This is the number.

Task two:
From the first clue, the number is one of these 16 **17** 18 19 20 21 22 23 24.

From the second clue, to make 30 from each of the four numbers requires additions:
4 + 26 , 13 + **17** , 15 + 15 , 17 + 13.

The only number fitting both clues is **17**. This is the number.

Task three:
From the first clue, the number is one of these 23 24 **25** 26 27 28.

From the second clue, a variety of different numbers can be made by adding together pairs of the numbers taken from 6 11 19 24. Only **6 + 19 = 25** gives a sum which matches one of the numbers from the first clue. All of the other additions create sums that are too large or too small.
                    The number is **25**.

Task four:
From the first clue, the number is one of these 41 42 43 44 **45** 46 47 48 49.

From the second clue, the only addition which gives one of these numbers is
10 + 35 = 45.
                    The number is **45**.

What number am I?

● Use the clues to find each number.

I am more than 2 but less than 10.
Add me to one of these numbers to make 25

I am number [ ]

I am more than 15 but less than 25.
Add me to one of these numbers to make 30

I am number [ ]

I am more than 22 but less than 29.
I can be made by adding together two of these numbers

I am number [ ]

I am more than 40 but less than 50.
I can be made by adding together two of these numbers

I am number [ ]

⟨10⟩ ⟨15⟩ ⟨25⟩ ⟨35⟩

● Make up a number problem of your own. Ask a friend to find
the number.

Maths for the More Able 2

Place value and addition

Learning objectives

- ◆ Add 10 to a two-digit number using knowledge of place value.
- ◆ Add a one-digit number to a multiple of 10.
- ◆ Add multiples of 10 to make totals greater than 100.

Resources

AS '100 total'

Teacher's notes

The activity involves children in using a flow chart and following a set of rules.

Children are presented with a number flow chart. They have to explore alternative routes that involve the addition of different numbers. A route starts at the top and follows the direction of the arrows to reach the end. A route cannot be retraced since this will go in the opposite direction to the arrows. Each circled number met on the route is added to make a total.

There are three parts to this activity:

'100 total'. The aim is to find the three different ways of getting a total of 100.

$$10 + \mathbf{30 + 50} + 10 = 100$$
$$10 + \mathbf{5 + 50 + 25} + 10 = 100$$
$$10 + \mathbf{30 + 35 + 15} + 10 = 100$$

Children should realise that since 10 is added at the start and 10 is added at the end then the middle numbers must add up to 80 (30 + 50 = 80; 5 + 50 + 25 = 80; 30 + 35 + 15 = 80). Also, if a number ending in five is added at one point then another number ending in five must be added later so the sum will end in zero.

The **largest number** is **150**. This is the route:

$$10 + \mathbf{30 + 50 + 35 + 15} + 10 = 150$$

This part of the activity involves calculating numbers greater than 100.

The **smallest number** is **70**. It can be made in two ways:

$$10 + \mathbf{50} + 10 = 70$$
$$10 + \mathbf{5 + 20 + 25} + 10 = 70$$

100 total

● Go from the start to the end in the direction of the arrows.
Add up as you go along.

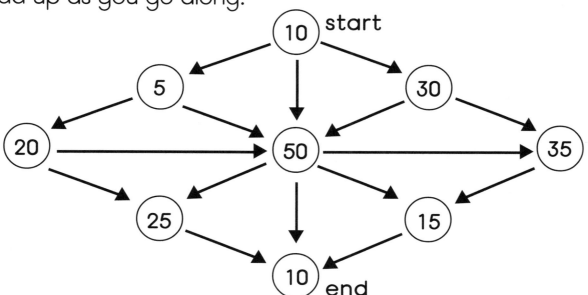

Example of a route: **Start → 5 → 50 → 35 → 15 → end**
10 + 5 + 50 + 35 + 15 + 10 = 125

● Find a route to give you a total of 100.
There are three routes:
Route 1 is 10 + _____ + 10 = 100
Route 2 is 10 + _____ + 10 = 100
Route 3 is 10 + _____ + 10 = 100

● What is the **largest** total you can make?

10 + _____ + 10

The total is _____

● What is the **smallest** total you can make?
Find two routes for the same total.
Route A is 10 + _____ + 10
Route B is 10 + _____ + 10.

The total is _____

Addition and subtraction strategies and money

Learning objectives

- ◆ Make decisions, check the effect of an operation, check by doing the inverse operation.
- ◆ Use and apply knowledge of adding and subtracting including the fact that subtraction is the inverse of addition.
- ◆ Add/subtract a one-digit number to/from a two-digit number.
- ◆ Add/subtract a two-digit number to/from a two-digit number.
- ◆ Subtract a three-digit number from a three-digit number.

Resources

AS 'Money pyramids'

Teacher's notes

There are two parts to this activity. Each part has three tasks involving addition and subtraction.

Children have to work out the numbers missing from **addition pyramids**. This involves the children in solving problems in a systematic way.

The first number to be worked out is 6p in the bottom row of boxes. Then 9p can be calculated for the box in the middle row. This then allows the final figure of 25p to be worked out.

25p
16p + **9p**
10p + **6p** + 3p

The first number to be worked out is 47p in the middle row. Then 29p can be calculated for the left-hand box in the bottom row. Finally, 10p is put in the right-hand box of the bottom row.

75p
47p + 28p
29p + 18p + **10p**

The first number to be worked out is 56p in the right-hand box of the middle row. Then 64p can be calculated for the left-hand box of the middle row. Finally, 33p can be worked out for the bottom row.

£1.20
64p + **56p**
33p + 31p + 25p

Children have to work out the numbers missing from **subtraction pyramids**. This involves the children in solving problems in a systematic way.

The first number to be worked out is 3p in the right-hand box of the middle row. Then 4p can be calculated for the right-hand box of the bottom row. Finally, 12p is put in the left-hand box of the bottom row.

2p
5p – **3p**
12p – 7p – **4p**

The first number to be worked out is 22p in the right-hand box of the middle row. Then 43p is calculated for the middle box of the bottom row. Finally, 21p can be calculated for the right-hand box of the bottom row.

1p
23p – **22p**
66p – **43p** – **21p**

The first number to be worked out is £2.40 for the left-hand box of the middle row. The top number, £1.25 can be calculated. Finally, £1.45 is calculated for the right-hand box of the bottom row.

£1.25
£2.40 – £1.15
£5.00 – £2.60 – **£1.45**

Money pyramids

● A money pyramid is made of boxes on top of each other.
Some of the boxes are empty.
Work out each missing number and write it in its box.
The numbers get smaller from left to right.

In **addition money pyramids** you add the two boxes next to each other.
The sum goes in the box above them.
This is a completed money pyramid.

	12p	
7p		5p
4p	3p	2p

12p = 7p + 5p
7p = 4p + 3p
5p = 3p + 2p

● Work out the missing numbers and complete the pyramids.

	p	
16p		p
10p	p	3p

	75p	
p		28p
p	18p	p

	£1.20	
p		p
p	31p	25p

In **subtraction money pyramids** you subtract the boxes next to each other. The difference goes in the box above.
This is a completed money pyramid.

	10p	
12p		2p
20p	8p	6p

10p = 12p – 2p
12p = 20p – 8p
2p = 8p – 6p

● Complete the pyramids.

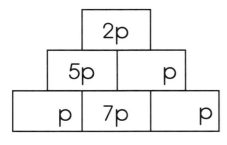

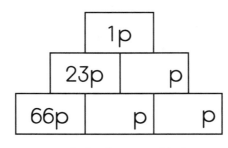

Length

Learning objectives

◆ Solve problems involving length.
◆ Understand and use the vocabulary relating to length.

Resources

AS 'Line routes'

Teacher's notes

This activity involves drawing line routes through a square grid.

Children should be told that the lines must not be drawn as diagonals.
They must be horizontal or vertical.

The length of a line is the number of squares it passes through, which must include the start and end squares.

The shortest route is 7 units.

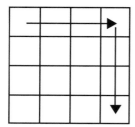

There are a number of different 7 unit routes.

The longest route is 15 units.

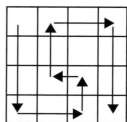

There are a number of different 15 unit routes. All 16 squares cannot be covered. There is always one missing.

The different routes which can be drawn have the following lengths:

7 units; 9 units; 11 units; 13 units; 15 units.

These are all odd numbers. It is not possible to draw a route from the start to the end with a length which is an even number of units.

Did any of the children discover this fact?

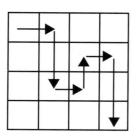

9 units in length

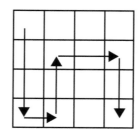

11 units in length

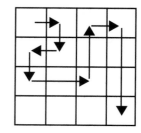

13 units in length

Line routes

This line passes through 9 squares.
It has a length of 9 units.

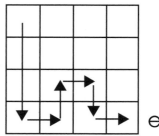

start

end

In the blank grids draw two lines from
the start to the end.
One line must be the shortest length possible.
The other line must be the longest length possible.
A line cannot move in a diagonal way.
It cannot go into a square more than once.

start 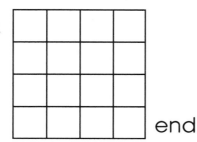 end

start 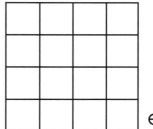 end

The shortest line is _____ units.   The longest line is _____ units.

● Use the blank grids to draw more routes with different
   lengths.

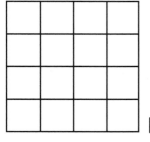 length _____ units

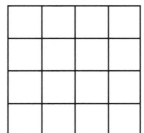 length _____ units

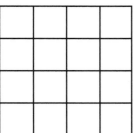 length _____ units

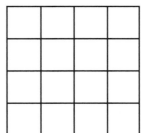 length _____ units

● Have you found anything interesting about all of these
   lengths?

Maths for the More Able 2

Shape and space, reasoning about shapes

Learning objectives

- ◆ Use 2-D shapes.
- ◆ Develop understanding of the properties of shapes.

Resources

AS 'Triangle maker'

Teacher's notes

This activity is about drawing lines inside one shape to create other shapes.

There are three parts to the activity.

In the first part there is a square and no triangles.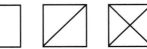
Drawing one diagonal line creates **two triangles**.
Drawing a second diagonal line creates another two triangles. There are now **four triangles**.

In the second part there are four squares.

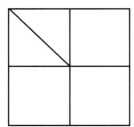

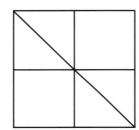

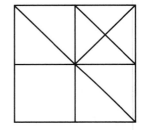

One diagonal line creates three squares and two triangles.

Two diagonal lines create two squares and four triangles.

Four diagonals create one square and eight triangles.

Children can draw the diagonals in different positions to make different patterns of squares and triangles.

The final part is about dividing up a rectangle into squares and triangles.

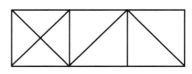

Two vertical lines create three squares.

Four diagonals create eight triangles and no squares.

This is wrong since one square remains.

Triangle maker

Here is a square.

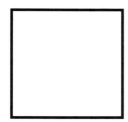

- How many triangles?

_____

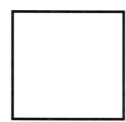

- Draw one diagonal line to make two triangles.

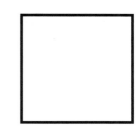

- Draw two diagonals. How many triangles?

_____

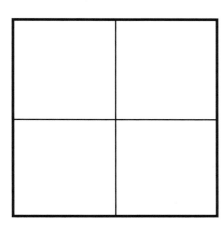

- Draw one diagonal to make three squares and two triangles.

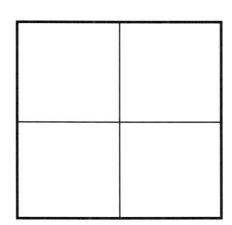

- Draw two diagonals to make two squares and four triangles.

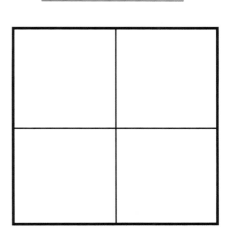

- Draw four diagonals to make one square and eight triangles.

This is a rectangle.

- Draw two lines to make three squares.
- Then draw four diagonals to make eight triangles with no squares.

Maths for the More Able 2

Reasoning about numbers

Learning objectives

◆ Solve word problems and explain methods of working.
◆ Recognise odd and even numbers.
◆ Recognise and explain general statements about odd numbers.
◆ Develop mental strategies.

Resources

AS 'Odd rules'

Teacher's notes

This activity is about testing four rules which apply to odd numbers.

It may be necessary to talk through each rule with the children so they understand fully what is meant.

Then ask how the rule might be tested.

What do you have to do? What numbers might you use?

Finally, how will you know if the rule is true or false?

The **first** rule is: *the sum of two odd numbers is always an even number.*

The **second** rule is: *the difference of two odd numbers is always an even number.*

Showing that these rules are true requires addition and subtraction of odd numbers.

Example: $5 + 7 = 12$ and $27 - 3 = 24$
odd + odd = even   odd – odd = even

The **third** rule is: *the sum of an odd and an even number is always an odd number.*

The **fourth** rule is: *the difference of an odd and an even number is always an odd number.*

Showing that these two rules are true involves using even numbers in the additions and subtractions.

Example: $37 + 6 = 43$ and $19 - 4 = 15$
odd + even = odd   odd – even = odd

For each of these rules ask the children to select different numbers and write down at least four calculations.

Odd rules

Here is a rule about odd numbers.

The sum of two odd numbers is always an even number.

- Think about what this means.
  Do you think it is true or false?_____

- Add some numbers to test this rule.

Here is another rule about odd numbers.

The difference of two odd numbers is always an even number.

- Is this rule true or false? _____

- Subtract some numbers to test this rule.

These are two more rules.

The sum of an odd and an even number is always an odd number.

The difference of an odd and an even number is always an odd number.

- Test these two rules by adding and subtracting numbers.

Addition and subtraction, mental calculation strategies

Learning objectives

◆ Understand subtraction and related vocabulary.
◆ Subtract a one-digit number from a multiple of 10.

Resources

AS 'Matching'

Teacher's notes

This activity is in three parts. The aim is to match up totals which have been made in different ways. The answer to each calculation is in brackets.

The **first** solution is:

20 – 8 **(12)**   15 + 2 **(17)**

30 – 5 **(25)**   17 + 4 **(21)**

19 – 2 **(17)**   7 + 5 **(12)**

40 – 9 **(31)**   19 + 6 **(25)**

30 – 12 **(18)** ——————— 11 + 7 **(18)**

The two that do not match are underlined.

The solution to the **second** set of numbers is:

50 – 3 **(47)**   15 + 15 **(30)**   19 + 21 **(40)** 70 – 25 **(45)**   23 + 27 **(50)**

30 +15 **(45)**   65 – 25 **(40)**   90 – 43 **(47)**   120 – 70 **(50)**   70 – 35 **(35)**

The solution to the **third** set of numbers is:

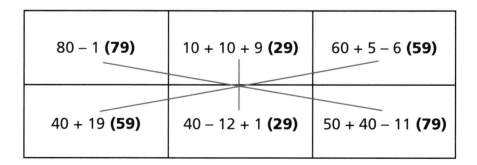

80 – 1 **(79)**	10 + 10 + 9 **(29)**	60 + 5 – 6 **(59)**
40 + 19 **(59)**	40 – 12 + 1 **(29)**	50 + 40 – 11 **(79)**

Matching

● Here are some subtractions and additions. Join the matched pairs with a line. One is done for you.

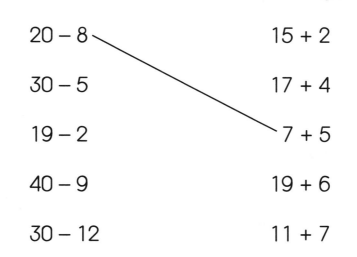

20 – 8	15 + 2
30 – 5	17 + 4
19 – 2	7 + 5
40 – 9	19 + 6
30 – 12	11 + 7

● Which do not match? _____ and _____ .

● Match four sums and differences on the top line with four on the bottom line. One on the top and one on the bottom do not match.

50 – 3   15 + 15   19 + 21   70 – 25   23 + 27

30 +15   65 – 25   90 – 43   120 – 70   70 – 35

● Match three pairs of squares.

80 – 1	10 + 10 + 9	60 + 5 – 6
40 + 19	40 – 12 + 1	50 + 40 – 11

Multiplication and division, mental calculation strategies

Learning objectives

- ◆ Understand that doubling and halving are inverse operations.
- ◆ Begin to halve multiples of 10 up to 100.
- ◆ Recognise patterns in halving multiples of 10.

Resources

AS 'Which pets?'

Teacher's notes

This activity is in the form of number stories.

These are the solutions to the problems:

Victoria has three cats and one bird (four pets and 14 legs).
There is only one solution. (3 x 4) + (1 x 2) = 14.
One pet must be a bird (feathered).

Daniel has two cats, one bird and two fish (five pets and 10 legs).
There is only one solution (2 x 4) + (1 x 2) = 10. There are two cats, two fish and one bird.
There cannot be three cats and three fish. Similarly, one cat and one fish would lead to three birds.

Gemma has one cat, one bird and two fish or three birds and one fish (four pets and six legs).
(1 x 4) + (1 x 2) = 6 or 3 x 2 = 6. There cannot be two cats since these have eight legs.

The solutions to Tariq's problem are best presented in a table.

Cats	Birds	Fish
2 (2 x 4 legs)	**0**	**4**
1 (4 legs)	**2** (2 x 2 legs)	**3**
0	**4** (4 x 2 legs)	**2**

The systematic approach is clearly seen. Start with two cats, one cat and no cats to work out the combinations.

Which pets?

There are five children. They have cats, birds and fish as pets. Find the types and numbers of pets owned by each child.

Sean has three pets. The total number of legs is two. A cat has four legs and a bird has two legs. Sean cannot have a cat. He must have one bird. Therefore, **Sean has 1 bird and 2 fish.**

- Victoria has four pets. The pets have a total of fourteen legs. Only one pet has feathers.

  Victoria has these pets: _____

- Daniel has five pets. The pets have a total of ten legs. He has more cats than birds.

  Daniel has these pets: _____

- Gemma has four pets. The pets have a total of six legs. There are two solutions.

  Gemma might have these pets: _____
  Gemma might have these pets: _____

- Tariq has six pets. The pets have a total of eight legs. There are three solutions.

  Tariq might have these pets: _____
  Tariq might have these pets: _____
  Tariq might have these pets: _____

- Make up a problem of your own.
  Ask a friend to find the pets.

Money and 'real-life' problems

Learning objectives

◆ Find totals and calculate change.
◆ Choose the appropriate operation.
◆ Explain ways of working.
◆ Make decisions and check results.

Resources

AS 'Which fruits?'

Teacher's notes

This problem-solving activity takes the form of three number stories.
In the first part there is only one possible solution:

2 bananas + 2 apples + 1 pear = 70p
2 x 15p   2 x 10p   20p

There must be two bananas to make the total end in a zero.

The second part is more open-ended in that the children do not know there are four solutions. These are:

1 banana + 4 apples = 55p
15p   + 4 x 10p

5p   **1 banana + 2 pears = 55p**
              15p   + 2 x 20p

of bananas (one or three) in order to get a total

from £1.00. This means that **85p** was spent.

anana, three bananas or five bananas were bought.
in a five.
cannot have been five bananas since they total 75p.

Try three bananas. They come to 45p which leaves 40p for two fruit. Two pears come to 40p. This is the answer.

3 bananas + 2 pears = 85p
3 x 15p   2 x 20p

Name: _____   Date: _____

Which fruits?

Here are three types of fruit. Each costs a different amount.

   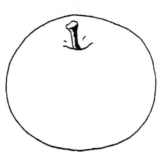   

banana 15p   *apple 10p*   *pear 20p*

● I want at least one of each fruit. What can I buy for exactly 70p?

_____

_____

● What can I buy for exactly 55p? _____

● There are different ways to spend exactly 55p. Find as many ways as you can.

_____

_____

● I buy five fruits and get 15p change from £1.00.

  What fruits did I buy? How did you work this out?

_____

_____

● Make a problem of your own. Ask a friend to find the answer.

Maths for the More Able 2

Length, making decisions and checking results

Learning objectives

◆ Solve a problem involving length – make decisions.
◆ Explain the work and record.
◆ Develop measuring skills using centimetres.

Resources

AS 'How many strips?'

Teacher's notes

This problem-solving activity is about fitting a number of short lengths on a longer length. The aim is to fit short lengths of paper strips on to a longer piece of card. This is done as a mathematical activity although it could easily be carried out as a practical exercise.

The activity is in three parts.

In the first part strips of paper measuring 2cm and 3cm have to be fitted on a 50cm piece of card. The number of 2cm and 3cm strips is to be the same.

It can be seen that 2cm + 3cm = 5cm. Each pair of paper strips measures 5cm. Consequently, 10 pairs of paper strips will fit on the card (10 x 5cm = 50cm). **Ten strips of paper measuring 2cm and 10 strips measuring 3cm will fit on a 50cm piece of card.**
As a final check: 10 x 2cm + 10 x 3cm = 20cm + 30cm = 50cm.

In the next part, the paper strips are 2cm and 4cm in length. Together they measure 6cm. This means that eight pairs of paper strips will fit on the 50cm piece of card (8 x 6cm = 48cm). There will be 2cm of card left uncovered. **Eight strips of paper measuring 2cm and eight strips of paper measuring 4cm will fit on a 50cm piece of card.**
As a final check: (8 x 2cm) + (8 x 4cm) = 16cm + 32cm = 48cm.

In the final part the card is 100cm long. The paper pieces are 4cm and 5cm long. A pair of paper strips has a length of 9cm. This means that 11 pairs will fit on the 100cm piece of card. There will be 1cm of card uncovered. **Eleven strips of paper measuring 4cm and 11 strips of paper measuring 5cm will fit on a 100cm piece of card.**
As a final check: (11 x 4cm) + (11 x 5cm) = 44cm + 55cm = 99cm.

This activity can be extended to three or four different lengths of paper strips.

How many strips?

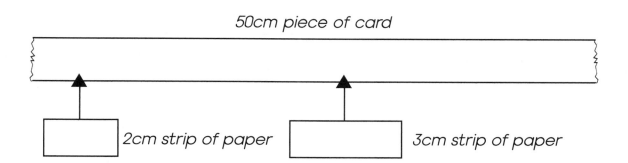

50cm piece of card

2cm strip of paper   *3cm strip of paper*

A piece of card is to be covered by strips. The strips are the same width as the card.
The strips come in two lengths: 2cm and 3cm.
You must use the same number of 2cm and 3cm strips.

● How many of each strip will you need to cover the card exactly?

2cm strips: _____   3cm strips:_____

You now have strips measuring 2cm and 4cm. Once again you must use the same number of each.

● How many of each will fit on the card? _____

● Will the card be covered totally? _____

Now you have a 100cm piece of card to cover. You have strips measuring 4cm and 5cm. Use exactly the same number of each.

● How many will fit on the card? _____

● Will the card be covered totally? _____

Handling data

Learning objectives

◆ Collect, record and interpret numerical data.
◆ Present the data in the form of a block graph and discuss results.

Resources

AS 'Dice sums', pair of dice.

Teacher's notes

This activity is in two parts. In the first part a pair of dice are thrown and each sum is recorded in a table. Alternatively, the sums can be recorded as a tally.

In the second part these results are recorded in a block diagram. The results are discussed and interpreted. Can children predict the form of the block graph? After throwing the dice about 50 times the general trends in the sums should be developing.

Throwing a sum of 2, 3, 4, or 5 is as equally likely as throwing a sum of 9, 10, 11 or 12.

Throwing a sum of 5, 6, 7 or 8 is much more likely than either of the other two.

This can be shown by counting the number of possible combinations of numbers to make the various sums.

Sum	Possible combinations of numbers	Total
2	1 + 1	1
3	1 + 2, 2 + 1	2
4	1 + 3, 3 + 1, 2 + 2	3
5	1 + 4, 4 + 1, 2 + 3, 3 + 2	4
		10
6	1 + 5, 5 + 1, 2 + 4, 4 + 2, 3 + 3	5
7	1 + 6, 6 + 1, 2 + 5, 5 + 2, 3 + 4, 4 + 3	6
8	2 + 6, 6 + 2, 3 + 5, 5 + 3, 4 + 4	5
		16
9	3 + 6, 6 + 3, 4 + 5, 5 + 4	4
10	4 + 6, 6 + 4, 5 + 5	3
11	5 + 6, 6 + 5	2
12	6 + 6	1
		10

Notice the triangular pattern created by the numbers of combinations.
This is because the numbers of combinations create a symmetrical pattern:

<u>**1 2 3 4 5 6 5 4 3 2 1**</u>
sum (2, 3, 4, 5) (6, 7, 8) (9,10,11,12)

The numbers of combinations to make 6, 7 and 8 are much greater than the others.

Dice sums

● Throw a pair of dice at least 50 times. Add the two numbers thrown and record the sum in the correct column in the table.

Sum of 2, 3, 4, 5	Sum of 6, 7, 8	Sum of 9, 10, 11,12
Total recorded ▢	Total recorded ▢	Total recorded ▢

● Put the totals in a block graph.

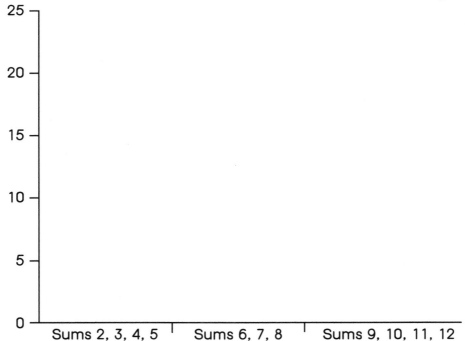

● What does your graph tell you about the three different sums?

_____

● Try to explain these results.

Counting, properties of numbers and number sequences

Learning objectives

◆ Count on or back in steps of a given size.
◆ Describe and continue number sequences.
◆ Make predictions.

Resources

AS 'Sequences'

Teacher's notes

This problem-solving activity is in three parts. In each part sequences have to be completed by filling in the missing numbers.

The first two sequences involve multiples of five. One sequence is completed by adding fives. The other sequence is completed by doubling each successive number.

| 5 | 10 | 15 | **20** | **25** | **30** | add 5 |

| 5 | 10 | 20 | **40** | **80** | **160** | double each number |

The next two sequences have numbers that are decreasing.

| 32 | 28 | **24** | 20 | **16** | **12** | subtract 4 |

| 32 | 16 | 8 | **4** | **2** | **1** | halve each number |

The final sequence has alternate missing numbers.

| 2 | **5** | 8 | **11** | 14 | **17** | add 3 |

Sequences

● Complete each sequence by filling in the missing numbers.

What is the rule for this sequence? _____

What is the rule for this sequence? _____

● The next two sequences are different. Think carefully about them.

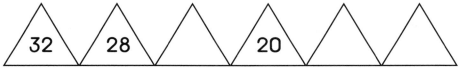

What is the rule for this sequence? _____

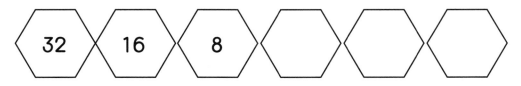

What is the rule for this sequence? _____

● The final sequence is more difficult. Think carefully.

What is the rule for this sequence? _____

● Make a sequence of your own. Ask a friend to find the missing numbers.

Place value and ordering

Learning objectives

- ◆ Read and write numbers to 100(+).
- ◆ Understand what each digit in a number represents.
- ◆ Understand the vocabulary of comparing and ordering numbers.
- ◆ Order numbers to 100(+).

Resources

AS 'Three numbers'

Teacher's notes

This problem-solving activity is about finding sets of numbers and placing them in order. Clues are provided about the numbers.

The activity is in two parts.

In part one the three new numbers are: **10** (8 + 2); **11** (7 + 4); **12** (9 + 3).

The three numbers can also be made in this way: 7 + 3; 9 + 2; 8 + 4

In part two the three new numbers are: **110** (50 + 60); **120** (50 + 70); **130** (50 + 80).

In part three the three new numbers are: **30**; **35**; **40**.
These numbers can be made in two ways:

$$30 = 15 + 15; 35 = 10 + 25; 40 = 20 + 20$$
or $$30 = 10 + 20; 35 = 15 + 20; 40 = 15 + 25.$$

Children might be able to make up their own number problem-solvers.

Three numbers

● Add pairs of numbers in the box to make three new numbers. Each number in the box can be used only once. The three new numbers are **one** apart from each other.

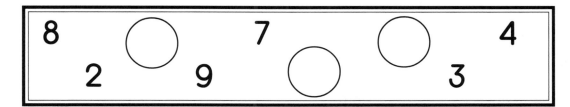

Write the three new numbers in order. _____

Explain how you worked them out.

_____

● Add pairs of numbers in the box to make three new numbers. The three new numbers are **ten** apart from each other.

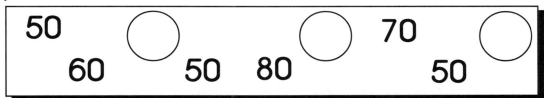

Write the three new numbers in order. _____

Explain how you worked them out.

_____

● Three new numbers are **five** apart from each other. There are two ways to find them.

```
┌ ─ ─ ─ ─ ─ ─ ─ ─ ─ ─ ─ ─ ─ ─ ─ ─ ┐
  10      ◯           ◯     25
│    20      15    15     ◯    20 │
└ ─ ─ ─ ─ ─ ─ ─ ─ ─ ─ ─ ─ ─ ─ ─ ─ ┘
```

Write the three new numbers in order. _____

Explain how you worked them out.

_____

Understanding addition and subtraction, mental calculation strategies

Learning objectives

- ◆ Understand the operation of addition and related vocabulary.
- ◆ Add a teens number to a two-digit number.
- ◆ Know that addition can be carried out in any order.
- ◆ Use patterns of similar calculations.

Resources

AS 'Whose throws?'

Teacher's notes

This problem-solving activity is quite easy when carried out in a systematic way.

Two things need to be done first:
- ● Count the number of squares already moved by Tara and Jack. These are Tara **30** and Jack **22**.
- ● Add up the six throws made so far.

These are $2 + 6 = 8$; $3 + 3 = 6$; $1 + 4 = 5$; $5 + 6 = 11$; $4 + 6 = 10$; $6 + 6 = 12$.

Next, work out which three numbers add up to 30 and which three add up to 22.

There is only one solution: $8 + 10 + 12 = 30$ (Tara) and $6 + 5 + 11 = 22$ (Jack).

Therefore, **Tara's throws were 2 + 6; 4 + 6; 6 + 6**

　　　　　and **Jack's throws were 3 + 3; 1 + 4; 5 + 6**.

Tara can finish with one more throw if she can get a total of **10**.

She needs **5 + 5, 4 + 6** or **6 + 4** to land exactly on the finish square.

Jack still has 18 squares to go. His first throw must take him to at least 12 squares from the finish square since $6 + 6 = 12$ is the maximum throw with two dice.
So he must get at least six with his first throw.
Let us say he throws $5 + 5 = $ **10**. He has **eight** left to get on his second throw.
He could get eight in five ways: **4 + 4, 5 + 3, 3 + 5, 6 + 2** or **2 + 6**.

Whose throws?

Tara and Jack, are playing a board game with a pair of dice.
Each child has thrown the dice three times.
Their counters are shown.

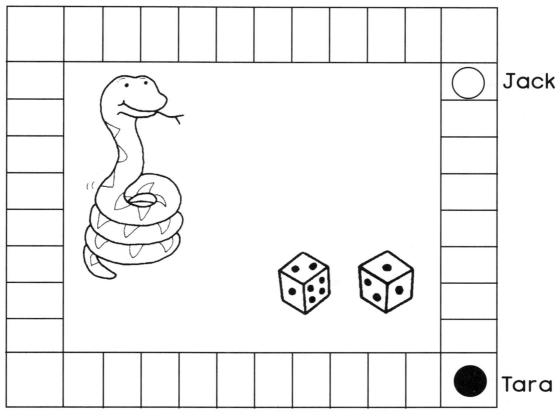

Jack

Tara

start here ↑ ↑ finish on this square
first square counts as one

- Can you work out which three pairs of numbers were
  thrown by Jack and which by Tara?

  The numbers were: 2 and 6; 3 and 3; 1 and 4; 5 and 6;
  4 and 6; 6 and 6.

  Tara threw _____   Jack threw _____

- Tara can finish in one throw. What number
  does she need on the two dice to land
  exactly on the finish?   _____

- Jack needs two throws to finish. What
  numbers might he get so he lands exactly
  on the finish?   _____

Money, making decisions and checking results

Learning objectives

◆ Solve money problems.
◆ Check calculations.

Resources

AS 'Money mountain'

Teacher's notes

This problem-solving activity is about adding small sums of money to get different totals.

The path to follow up 'money mountain' which gives the smallest total is

$$2p + 3p + 3p + 1p + 4p = 13p$$

The path to follow up 'money mountain' which gives the largest total is

$$5p + 2p + 5p + 2p + 4p = 18p$$

A total of 15p can be achieved from any of the starting numbers.

$$3p + 1p + 5p + 2p + 4p = 15p$$

$$5p + 2p + 3p + 1p + 4p = 15p$$

$$4p + 3p + 3p + 1p + 4p = 15p$$

$$4p + 2p + 3p + 2p + 4p = 15p$$

$$2p + 5p + 3p + 1p + 4p = 15p$$

$$2p + 5p + 3p + 1p + 4p = 15p$$

The total must be 15p because this is the only figure that the routes on the extreme left and right (starting at 3p and 2p respectively) can produce.

Will any of the children realise this?

NB There are two paths possible starting from 4p. The second route gives the answer to the question, 'Can you find a sixth path?'.

Money mountain

- Start at any of the squares on the bottom of 'money mountain'. Move up one square at a time until you reach the top. As you move upwards add the money on each square.

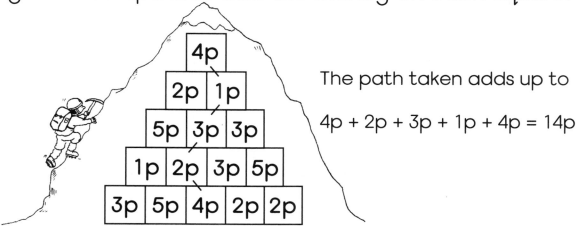

The path taken adds up to

4p + 2p + 3p + 1p + 4p = 14p

- Your path must only go up and cannot go back or sideways.

  Find a path which gives the lowest total.

  My path is _____ . The total is _____ .

- Find another path which gives the largest total.

  My path is _____ . The total is _____ .

- There is one total that you can get starting anywhere on the bottom.

  What is this total? _____ .

- Write down the five paths, starting with each of the five numbers.

  3p + ____ + ____ + ____ + 4p = 15p

  5p + ____ + ____ + ____ + 4p = 15p

  4p + ____ + ____ + ____ + 4p = 15p

  2p + ____ + ____ + ____ + 4p = 15p

  2p + ____ + ____ + ____ + 4p = 15p

- Can you find a sixth path? Write it down. _____

Mass

Learning objectives

- ◆ Solve measurement problems: explain methods and reasoning.
- ◆ Understand and use vocabulary related to mass.
- ◆ Measure and compare.

Resources

AS 'Balancing shapes'

Teacher's notes

This problem-solving activity is about the equivalence in mass of different shapes. The first two drawings provide the key to these problems. Circles are used as the basic unit.

2 squares balance 12 circles so **1 square = 6 circles**.

2 triangles balance 1 square. Which is the same as 2 triangles balance 6 circles. So **1 triangle = 3 circles**.

The solutions are given. The shapes to be added are in brackets on the correct side of the balance.

Problem 1
  6 circles = 1 triangle (**+ 1 triangle**)　*or*　6 circles = 1 triangle (**+ 3 circles**)

Problem 2
  1 square = 1 triangle + 1 circle (**+ 2 circles**)

Problem 3
  3 triangles = 1 square (**+ 1 triangle**)　*or*　3 triangles = 1 square (**+ 3 circles**)

Problem 4
  1 triangle (**+ 2 triangles**) = 1 square + 3 circles　*or*　1 triangle (**+ 6 circles**) =
  1 square + 3 circles　*or*　1 triangle (**+ 1 square**) = 1 square + 3 circles

The final problem is solved by first working out the total number of circles.

3 squares + 2 triangles + 6 circles = 18 circles + 6 circles + 6 circles = 30 circles.

To balance, there must be 15 circles in each pan.

One solution is　**2 squares + 1 triangle = 1 square + 1 triangle + 6 circles**
　　　　　　　　　(12 circles)　(3 circles)　　　(6 circles)　(3 circles)

An interesting question is to ask children why one square, one triangle and six circles cannot be balanced. Add up the circles. There are 15 circles. This cannot give an equal number on each side so these shapes cannot be balanced.

Balancing shapes

The circles and squares are equally balanced. So are the triangles and square.

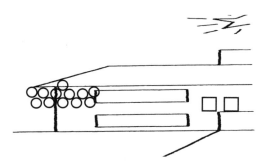
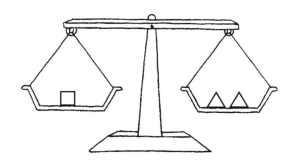

● Draw the number of shapes, in the correct pan, to make these balance:

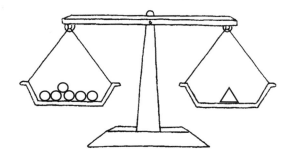
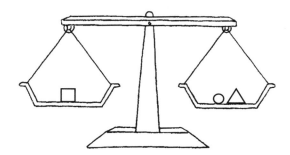

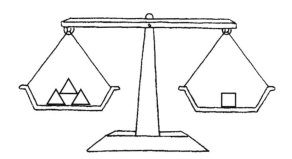
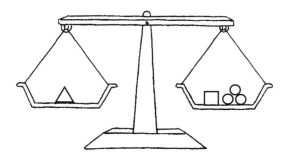

● You have three squares, two triangles and six circles. Draw in the shapes to make them balance.

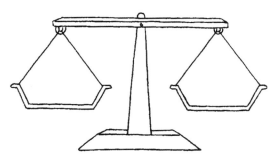

Shape and space

Learning objectives

◆ Solve problems and recognise patterns.
◆ Recognise and describe line symmetry.
◆ Complete symmetrical patterns.

Resources

AS 'Symmetry pictures'

Teacher's notes

In this activity children have three half-completed pictures to finish. They have to complete each picture by drawing the reflected image on the opposite side of the mirror line.

The three pictures are night-time, robot and computer. Each picture has a variety of shapes incorporated in it.

After completing the drawings, the children might like to colour them in.

Symmetry pictures

● Complete each picture by drawing the second half on the empty side of the mirror line.

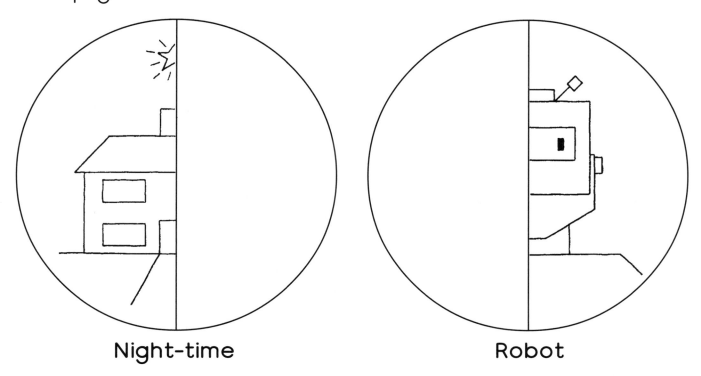

Night-time   Robot

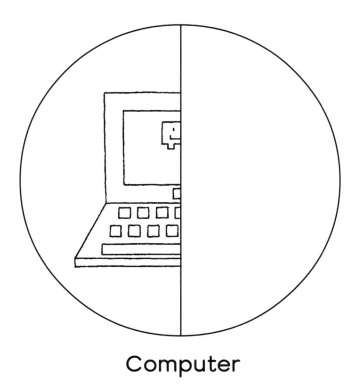

Computer

Counting and properties of numbers, reasoning about numbers

Learning objectives

- ◆ Recognise odd and even numbers.
- ◆ Recognise a pattern, generalise and make a prediction.
- ◆ Explain reasoning.

Resources

AS 'Odd reverse'

Teacher's notes

This activity is about taking a two-digit odd number, reversing it and then adding the two numbers together.

Example, 45 reverses to give 54. So **45 + 54 = 99**.

The two new digits (99) must be the same since reversing means the original two digits are added twice (5 + 4 = 9 and 4 + 5 = 9). Will this explanation occur to the children?

The same reasoning applies to an even two-digit number. For example 54 reverses to give 45. Children may realise this during the activity.

The interesting thing about this activity is the way in which patterns of numbers develop.

Total of 55	Total of 99	Total of 33	Total of 77
23 + 32; 41 + 14	27 + 72; 45 + 54; 63 + 36; 81 + 18	21 + 12	25 + 52; 43 + 34; 61 + 16

All the original odd numbers reverse to make an even number. The original two-digit odd number must have an even number as its first digit so that the final sum is odd (33, 55, 77, 99). This follows the rule: even number + odd number = odd number.

The creation of even numbers is even more interesting.

Total of 44	Total of 66	Total of 88
13 + 31 or 31 + 13	15 + 51 or 51 + 15	17 + 71 or 71 + 17; 35 + 53 or 53 + 35
(22 + 22 also gives 44)	(33 + 33 and 24 + 42 also give 66)	(26 + 62 and 44 + 44 also give 88)

Each of the original two-digit odd numbers has an odd number as its first digit. The two newly created digits are even. This follows the rule: odd number + odd number = even number. The number 22 is made from 11 since 11 + 11 = 22.

Finally, there are more interesting things to discover with other two-digit numbers that produce three-digit numbers.

For example, **37** gives 37 + 73 = **110**; **47** gives 47 + 74 = **121**; **57** gives 57 + 75 = **132**; **67** gives 67 + 76 = **143**; **77** gives 77 + 77 = **154**

The resulting three-digit numbers increase by 11.

Try other numbers like 29, 39, 49, 59 etc. or 28, 38, 48, 58, etc. These also increase by 11.

Odd reverse

Take a two-digit odd number, **23**. It can be reversed to make **32**. Add these two numbers together, 23 + 32 = 55.

Try this with another two-digit odd number, **81**. It reverses to make **18**.
Add these two numbers together, 81 + 18 = 99.

The new numbers made in this way are **55** and **99**. Their digits are the same.

● Make a list of other odd numbers which will make 55 and 99 in this way.

● Can you explain why numbers with the same digits are made?

_____

_____

● Try making some even two-digit numbers like 66 and 88.

● How do you know when you are going to make an even number?

_____

_____

Addition and subtraction, place value, mental calculation

Learning objectives

◆ Add and subtract multiples of 10 to/from a two-digit number.
◆ Use understanding of place value and patterns of related calculations.
◆ Add a two-digit number to a multiple of 10.
◆ Understand that addition can be carried out in any order and that this can make mental calculation more efficient.

Resources

AS 'Missing symbols'

Teacher's notes

In this activity children are presented with incomplete equations. The symbols + or – are missing. These symbols have to be put in the empty circles to complete the equations.

Each of the first two equations has one missing symbol. The same numbers are used in both equations but the totals are different. The solutions are:

$$24 - 5 = 19 \qquad\qquad 24 + 5 = 29$$

The next four equations have two symbols missing from each of them. Once again, the same numbers are used in all four equations. Children can explore the different ways in which these numbers can be added and subtracted to get different totals. The solutions are:

$$20 + 7 + 3 = 30; \ 20 + 7 - 3 = 24; \ 20 - 7 + 3 = 16; \ 20 - 7 - 3 = 10$$

The final two equations have three symbols missing from each of them.

$$100 - 50 - 40 - 10 = 0$$

$$100 + 50 - 40 - 10 = 100; \ 100 - 50 + 40 + 10 = 100$$

For a total of 100 there are two possible solutions. Will the children realise this?

It is possible to get a total of 200. All the numbers are added together: $100 + 50 + 40 + 10 = 200$.

It is not possible to get a total of 50.

Missing symbols

These number sentences can be completed by putting a + or - sign in each circle.
Example:

$$20 \bigcirc 5 = 15 \qquad 30 \bigcirc 3 = 33$$

Put a minus sign in this circle.　　　Put a plus sign in this circle.

● Each of these number sentences has one missing symbol:

$$24 \bigcirc 5 = 19 \qquad 24 \bigcirc 5 = 29$$

● These number sentences each have two symbols missing:

$$20 \bigcirc 7 \bigcirc 3 = 30 \qquad 20 \bigcirc 7 \bigcirc 3 = 24$$

$$20 \bigcirc 7 \bigcirc 3 = 16 \qquad 20 \bigcirc 7 \bigcirc 3 = 10$$

● These number sentences each have three symbols missing:

$$100 \bigcirc 50 \bigcirc 40 \bigcirc 10 = 0$$

$$100 \bigcirc 50 \bigcirc 40 \bigcirc 10 = 100$$

● Is it possible to make 200 from the number sentence above? If so, write it down. _____

● Is it possible to make 50 from the number sentence above? If so, write it down. _____

Mutiplication and division and 'real-life' problems

Learning objectives

◆ Develop understanding of multiplication and division.
◆ Recognise and interpret situations as multiplication and explain reasons.
◆ Write the appropriate sentence for a problem/context.

Resources

AS 'Cars and scooters'

Teacher's notes

These problem-solving tasks are in the form of number stories. Children have to find how many cars and scooters have travelled down a road. The numbers of each vehicle can be worked out from the total number of wheels and other clues. Children have to explore the various combinations in order to find the correct numbers of cars and scooters. Many of the combinations can be quickly worked out mentally.

Children need to be aware that a car has four wheels and a scooter has two.

The solutions are:

9.00am-9.15am. A total of four vehicles and 12 wheels.
The number of cars must be less than three since four cars have 16 wheels and three cars have 12 wheels. Try two cars.
Two cars have eight wheels. This leaves two scooters which have four wheels in total.
This is the answer: **2 cars + 2 scooters.**

9.15am-9.30am. A total of four vehicles and 10 wheels.
Try one car. This has four wheels. Add three scooters which have a total of six wheels.
This is the answer: **1 car + 3 scooters.**

The next two problems are more difficult.

9.30am-10am. A total of 40 wheels and twice as many scooters as cars.
Four, six and eight scooters would lead to too small a number of wheels.
There cannot be nine scooters because this would lead to five and a half cars.
Now try 10 scooters and five cars. A total of (10 x 2) + (5 x 4) wheels = 40 wheels.
This is the answer: **10 scooters + 5 cars.**

This long trial-and-improvement method can be shortened if children realise the following fact. For each car there are two scooters.
1 car + 2 scooters = 4 + 4 = 8 wheels and 8 wheels x 5 = 40 wheels.
There are 5 x (1 car + 2 scooters) or 5 cars and 10 scooters.

10am-11am. A total of 26 wheels with two more cars than scooters.
Four cars and two scooters lead to too small a total of wheels.
Try five cars and three scooters. (5 x 4) + (3 x 2) wheels = 26 wheels.
This is the answer: **5 cars + 3 scooters.**

Cars and scooters

Cars and scooters travel down a road. For each question, work out how many cars and how many scooters there were and explain how you worked it out.

● Between 9:00am and 9:15am there was a total of 4 vehicles. There were 12 wheels on these vehicles.

_____

_____

● Between 9:15am and 9:30am there were another 4 vehicles. This time there were only 10 wheels on the vehicles.

_____

_____

● Between 9:30am and 10am there were twice as many scooters as cars. The total number of wheels was 40.

_____

_____

● Between 10am and 11am there were 2 more cars than scooters. There was a total of 26 wheels.

_____

_____

● Write your own problem. Ask a friend to find out how many cars and scooters passed down the road.

Time

Learning objectives

◆ Use and understand vocabulary related to time.
◆ Solve simple problems relating to time.

Resources

AS 'What time?'

Teacher's notes

These number stories present problems that involve simple calculations relating to time.

These are the answers to the problems:

It is possible that Faraj had no sleep, or slept for 24 hours, but most likely, **Faraj went to bed at 7pm and got up at 7am. He had slept for 12 hours.**

Thomas starts painting at 8.30am.
He paints for a total of 30 minutes + 1 hour = $1\frac{1}{2}$ hours.
This means that **Thomas finishes at 10am**.

At 1pm Thomas does more painting.
He paints for a total time of 30 minutes + 3 x 30 minutes = (30 + 90) minutes = 120 minutes.
This is equivalent to two hours. So **Thomas finishes at 3pm**.

At 6pm Thomas starts painting more chairs which take 30 minutes each. He can complete three chairs in $1\frac{1}{2}$ hours. This takes him to 7.30pm. Thomas cannot finish another chair before 7.45pm. So **Thomas can finish three chairs by 7.45pm.**

Mrs Potter should arrive at work at 8.30am.
If **the clock at work** says 9am then it could be wrong. It **could be 30 minutes fast**. Or **the clock at home** could be wrong. It could be **30 minutes slow**. It might even have stopped at 8.00am.

What time?

These stories are about time.

- Faraj goes to bed at 7 o'clock and gets up at 7 o'clock. Has Faraj had no sleep? Explain your answer.

_____

_____

- At 8:30am Thomas starts to paint a door. This takes 1 hour. Then Thomas paints a chair. This takes 30 minutes. At what time does Thomas finish the painting? _____

- At 1pm Thomas does more painting. First he paints another chair. This takes 30 minutes. Then Thomas paints a wooden table. This takes him three times as long as the chair to paint. At what time does Thomas finish painting the table?

_____

- At 6pm Thomas starts to paint more chairs. How many chairs can he finish by 7:45pm?

_____

- When Mrs Potter leaves home her clock says 8:00am. Her journey to work takes exactly 30 minutes. When she arrives at work the clock says 9:00am.

  How might you explain this?

_____

Problems involving measures

Learning objectives

- ◆ Find solutions to simple mass word problems and explain methods and ways of working.
- ◆ Understand and use vocabulary associated with mass.
- ◆ Understand equivalence.

Resources

AS 'Bags of sweets'

Teacher's notes

Data on the cost of different amounts of sweets (by mass) is presented in a table.

Children use this data to work out the answers to three problems in number story form.

Mint toffees cost 50p for 20g. If £2.00 is spent then this is equal to 4 x 50p.

So the amount of sweets bought will be 4 x 20g = **80g**.

Lemon fizzies cost 50p for 50g. **Fruit drops** cost 50p for 20g.

Since 2 x 50p = £1.00. Then 2 x 50g of Lemon fizzies and 2 x 20g of Fruit drops are bought.

100g of Lemon fizzies + 40g of Fruit drops are bought. **A total mass of 140g**.

Orange chews cost 50p for 50g. **Mint toffees** cost 50p for 20g.

Since 4 x 50p = £2.00, then 4 x 50g of Orange chews and 4 x 20g of Mint toffees are bought.

200g of Orange chews and 80g of Mint toffees are bought.

The **Orange chews are** 200g – 80g = **120g heavier than Mint toffees**.

Bags of sweets

The table has the prices of different sweets. The sweets are sold in grams.

Types of sweets	Cost	Amount of sweets
Lemon fizzies	50p	50g
Orange chews	50p	50g
Fruit drops	50p	20g
Mint toffees	50p	20g

● Use the table to work out some problems.

What amount of Mint toffees can be bought for £2.00?

_____

You spend £1.00 on Lemon fizzies and £1.00 on Fruit drops. What amount of sweets have you bought?

_____

You spend £2.00 on Orange chews and £2.00 on Mint toffees. The Orange chews weigh more than the Mint toffees. How much heavier are the Orange chews than the Mint toffees?

_____

Make up a problem for a friend to work out.

Counting and properties of numbers

Learning objectives

◆ Count in twos, fives and tens.
◆ Recognise multiples of two, five and 10 and explain patterns.
◆ Recognise that some numbers can be a multiple of more than one number.

Resources

AS 'Which multiples win?'

Teacher's notes

This activity is about multiples of four and five. It is in two parts.

In the first part children have to make a guess. On a pair of dice, are there more ways to make multiples of four or five?
Then they have to identify the different ways of making these multiples.

There are more ways to make multiples of four than multiples of five on a pair of dice.

These ways are:

Multiples of four: 1 + 3; 3 + 1; 2 + 2; 2 + 6; 6 + 2; 3 + 5; 5 + 3; 4 + 4; 6 + 6 (nine ways)

Multiples of five: 1 + 4; 4 + 1; 2 + 3; 3 + 2; 4 + 6; 6 + 4; 5 + 5 (seven ways)

This activity can also be used to investigate multiples of twos and threes.

In the second part children have to identify the multiples of four and five between one and 20.
These multiples are then added to make two sums.

Multiples of four 4 + 8 + 12 + 16 + 20 = **60**

Multiples of five 5 + 10 + 15 + 20 = **50**

The sum of the multiples of four is greater than the sum of the multiples of five.

The sum of the multiples of four between 40 and 50 is **40 + 44 + 48 = 132**.
The sum of the multiples of five between 40 and 50 is **40 + 45 + 50 = 135**.

The sum of multiples of five is greater than the sum of multiples of four.

Which multiples win?

You can make the same total with two dice in different ways. For example, 6 can be made in five ways:

$$5 + 1; \ 1 + 5; \ 2 + 4; \ 4 + 2; \ 3 + 3$$

● Reuben thinks there are more ways to make multiples of 5 than multiples of 4 on a pair of dice. Do you think Reuben is right or wrong? Work out the different ways to make multiples of 4 and 5.

_____

_____

_____

● Francesca writes down all of the multiples of 4 between 1 and 20 and adds them together. Then she does the same for all the multiples of 5 between 1 and 20. Which sum do you think will be greater? Work out the two sums.

_____

_____

_____

● Would Francesca get the same answer if she added the multiples of 4 and of 5 between 40 and 50? Work it out for yourself.

_____

_____

_____

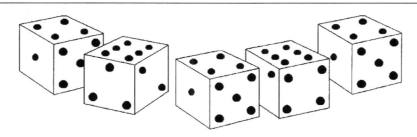

Place value, estimating and rounding

Learning objectives

◆ Understand and use the vocabulary of comparing and ordering numbers.
◆ Give the number that lies halfway between two others on a number line.

Resources

AS 'Halfway'

Teacher's notes

This activity is in two parts. In each part two children are playing a scoring game. Their present scores have to be calculated and how far each child is from the halfway point.

In the first game the halfway point is 25.

Angela has scored 18 and Sam has scored 15.

To reach the halfway point Angela must score seven more and Sam must score 10 more.

In the second game the halfway point is 50.

Angela has scored 10 + 10 + 10 + 10 + 8 (one ball scores 0) = **48**.

Sam has scored 10 + 10 + 8 + 8 + 8 + 8 = **52**.

This means that both Angela and Sam are two away from the halfway point. Angela has two to go and Sam has passed it by two.

The children are equally close to the halfway point.

Halfway

Angela and Sam are playing a game with a dice and a set of numbers. The numbers are 0 to 50 written on a strip of paper.

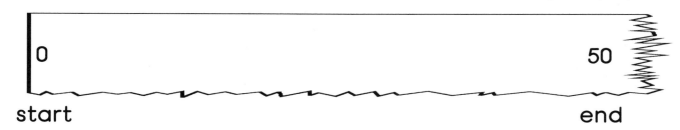

0   50

start   **end**

The children take turns to throw the dice.
Angela gets 5, 4, 3, 6. Sam gets 2, 4, 4, 5. Their scores are added up.

- How many more does Angela need to reach the halfway mark? _____

- How many more does Sam need to reach the halfway mark? _____

- On the strip write the halfway mark and the positions of Angela and Sam.

In another game Angela and Sam are throwing balls at a board. The first to reach 100 wins. They have each thrown six balls.

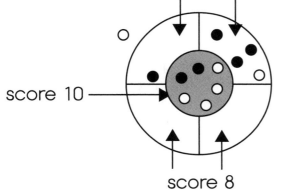

score 8

score 10

score 8

○ Angela's throws

● Sam's throws

No score for a ball outside the large circle.

- Who is nearer to halfway? Explain your answer.

_____

_____

Understanding subtraction, mental calculation strategies

Learning objectives

◆ Extend understanding of the operations of subtraction and addition.
◆ Subtract a one-digit number from a 20s number.
◆ Find unknowns.

Resources

AS 'Take aways'

Teacher's notes

This activity is about subtracting from a starting number to end up with another number.

In the first problem 24 is to be reduced to 12 by taking away two numbers. Children have to find these two numbers amongst a set of five numbers. A total of 12 is being taken away from 24. There is only one way to get 12 from two of the numbers listed. The numbers are nine and three.

The answer is 24 – 9 – 3 = 12

The next problem involves finding three numbers which are equal to 16. Taking these away from 18 will give two. Once again, there is only one way of doing this. The numbers are eight, six and two.

The answer is 18 – 8 – 6 – 2 = 2

There are two solutions to the next problem. In other words, there are two ways to get a total of 20 using three of the given numbers.
The numbers can be 10, six and four or nine, six and five.

The answers are 25 – 10 – 6 – 4 = 5 *or* 25 – 9 – 6 – 5 = 5

It is not possible to go from 20 to 10 by subtracting three of the given numbers. In other words, a total of 10 cannot be made from any three of the given numbers. The only way to get a total from three of these numbers would involve addition as well as subtraction

8 + 6 – 4 = 10

Take aways

Go from 10 to 1 by taking away two of the numbers in the box. Which numbers do you use?

10 | 2 4 5 6 8 | 1

You must take away a total of 9. The only two numbers that do this are 4 and 5.

$$10 - 5 - 4 = 1$$

- Go from 24 to 12 by taking away **two** of the numbers in the box. Which numbers do you use?

24 : 3 4 5 6 9 : 12

$$24 - \quad - \quad = 12$$

- Go from 18 to 2 by taking away **three** of the numbers in the box. Which numbers do you use?

18 | 2 4 6 8 12 | 2

$$18 - \quad - \quad - \quad = 2$$

- Go from 25 to 5 by taking away **three** of the numbers in the box. There are two ways of doing this. Try to find both ways.

25 | 4 5 6 8 9 10 | 5

$$25 - \quad - \quad - \quad = 5 \quad \text{and} \quad 25 - \quad - \quad - \quad = 5$$

- Can you go from 20 to 10 by taking away **three** of the numbers in the box?

20 | 2 3 4 6 7 8 | 10

- Explain your answer. _____

Money and 'real-life' problems, making decisions and checking results

Learning objectives

◆ Extend understanding of the operations of subtraction and addition.
◆ Subtract a one-digit number from a 20s number.
◆ Find unknowns.

Resources

AS 'Coin throws'

Teacher's notes

This problem-solving activity involves simple money calculations.

Children have to work out how much is won or lost on a board game.

In the first problem a player throws a 2p and a 10p. Both win so the money is doubled.

The player gets back $(2 \times 10p) + (2 \times 2p) = 20p + 4p = $ **24p**.

In the next problem a player throws a 10p and a 2p. The 10p wins but the 2p loses. This means the player gets back $2 \times 10p = 20p$.
Since the player started with $10p + 2p = 12p$ then **the money gained is** $20p - 12p = $ **8p**.

In the final problem a player throws three coins. These are two 10p coins and a 20p. Two coins lose but the third wins. The player gets back the amount thrown. Since $(2 \times 10p) + 20p = 40p$ was thrown the player must get 40p back. The only way this can happen is if the 20p coin wins. The money is doubled so $2 \times 20p = 40p$.

Therefore, the 20p coin won.

Coin throws

At a fair there is a game where players throw coins.

If a coin lands on a **WIN** square then the player gets two coins back. The money is doubled.

If a coin lands on a **LOSE** square then that coin is lost.

WIN	LOSE
LOSE	WIN

Example:

A player throws a 5p and a 2p coin. He gets 4p back. This means the 2p coin won but the 5p coin lost.

● A player throws a 2p and a 10p. How much will she get back if both coins win?

_____

● Another player throws a 10p and a 2p. The 10p wins but the 2p loses. The player has more money than before the game. How much more?

_____

● One player throws three coins. These are two 10p coins and a 20p coin. Two of the coins lose and one wins. The player gets back the same amount as was thrown. Which coin won?

_____

● Make up a coin throwing problem for a friend to work out.

Shape and space

Learning objectives

◆ Use vocabulary for direction and movement.
◆ Recognise quarter, half and whole turns.
◆ Know that a quarter turn is a right angle.
◆ Give instructions for movement in straight lines and for right-angle turns.

Resources

AS 'Making deliveries'

Teacher's notes

This activity is about working out routes between a number of points.

The aim is to find the shortest routes to be taken when delivering milk and letters. These two routes have to be drawn on the plan as straight lines. This means that lines are joined at right angles.

How can the lengths of different routes be compared?
One way is to use a house as the unit of length. Another way is actually to measure the length of the lines using a ruler.

Drawing two sets of lines on the plan can lead to confusion.
How might children show that one line is for milk and the other is for letters?
One simple way is to colour code the lines. Red might be used for one and blue for the other.

In order to give directions to go from A to B it is useful if the roads are named. What about numbering or lettering houses?
Will any children suggest these things?
Also, will any children use the arrow pointing north to help them in giving clearer directions? For example, stand with back to house A facing north. Walk across road to house X. Stop.
Make a right-angle turn anti-clockwise (to the left) ....etc.

Making deliveries

Each morning milk and letters are delivered to houses in a number of roads.

Milk is delivered to houses marked with a circle ●

Letters are delivered to houses marked with a square ■

● Work out the shortest route for delivering the milk and the shortest route for delivering the letters. Draw these routes as straight lines on the plan.

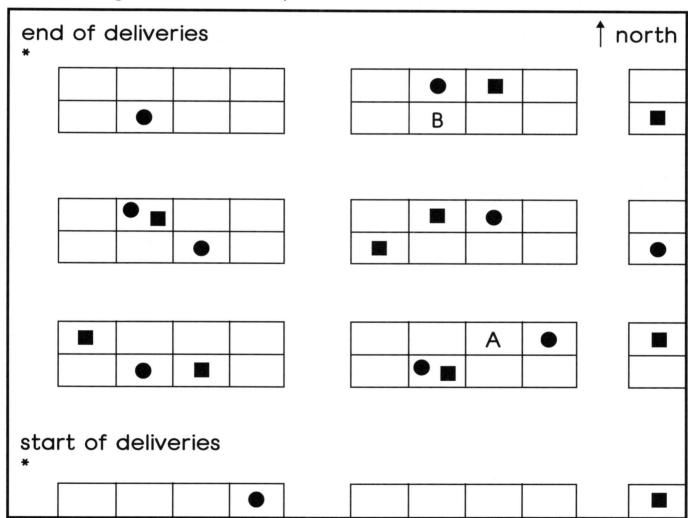

● How would you direct someone who wants to go from house A to house B?

_____

_____

Shape and space, reasoning about shapes

Learning objectives

- ◆ Recognise, name, describe and group common 3-D shapes using the appropriate vocabulary.
- ◆ Relate 3-D shapes to 2-D pictures.

Resources

AS 'Colouring in'

Teacher's notes

This problem-solving activity is in two parts.

The first part is about visualising a two-dimensional pattern and looking ahead to avoid colouring in adjacent areas in the same colour.
Discuss the colouring rule with the children so they fully understand what it means.

A useful strategy is to pencil in numbers lightly on the patterns prior to colouring in. This helps avoid mistakes and spoiling patterns by rushing into the activity. Examine the position of the numbers to see if the same number is in adjacent areas. If everything looks okay then colour in using the colour code (example: 1 = green, 2 = red, 3 = blue, etc.).

The following are solutions to the square patterns:

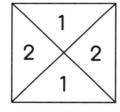

two colours

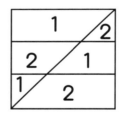

two colours

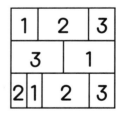

three colours

In the second part extra care must be taken because the two long edges will be joined when making a cylinder. Explain the use of the shaded strip (tab).

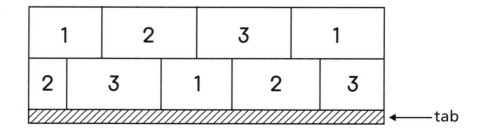

Three colours are the minimum number to colour in the pattern on the rectangle.

Colouring in

● Colour each pattern using as few colours as possible. Follow the rule:

Areas next to each other must be in different colours.

Areas meeting at a point are not next to each other.

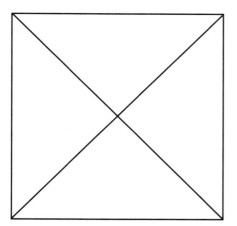 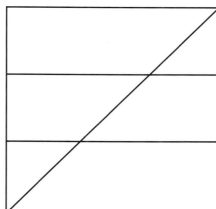 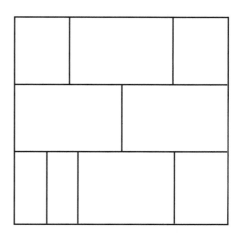

● How many colours did you use for each square?

_____   _____   _____

● After colouring in this rectangle it will be cut out, turned and joined along its long edges to make a cylinder. Do not colour in the shaded strip. This is for joining the two edges.

Think carefully because the two long edges will be joined later. Two areas next to each other must not have the same colour.

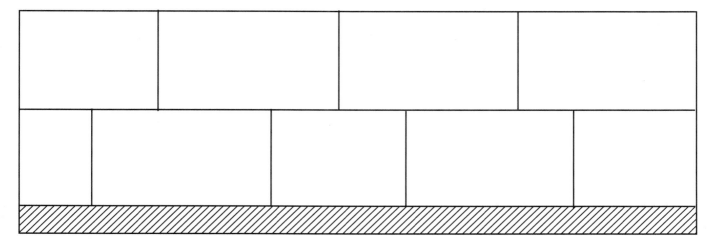

Counting and properties of numbers, reasoning about numbers

Learning objectives

◆ Solve mathematical problems or puzzles.
◆ Explain methods of calculation and reasoning orally.
◆ Recognise and use symbols for unknowns.

Resources

AS 'Addition triangles'

Teacher's notes

This problem-solving activity is about working out the missing numbers and putting them in their circles. The pairs of numbers on the corners of a triangle are added to make the number at the centre of a side. Ensure that children understand this rule.

The first triangle has two sides which are almost complete.
One number is missing from the corner which is common to these sides.

$$4 + ? = 9 \text{ and } 2 + ? = 7$$

The missing number must be **five.** This is written in.
The other missing number is 4 + 2 = **6**.

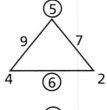

The next triangle can only be solved by putting **five** at each corner. Any other combinations such as 6/4 and 8/2 do not work. Children might like to try different combinations to see what happens.

With the third triangle begin at the base since this has two numbers in it.

$$? + 6 = 9$$

The missing number is **three**. This allows the right-hand side to be completed

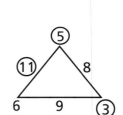

$$? + 3 = 8$$

The missing number is **five**. The final missing number is, therefore, 5 + 6 = **11**.

The two triangles with no numbers in them are completed by using a little logic to begin with. In the first triangle **one** must be at one corner. It cannot be the sum of two numbers. Number **six** must be in the centre of two sides because if it is at a corner then a sum greater than six would be made at the centre. Number **five** must be at the centre of a side. It cannot be at a corner to make six with one. Why? Try it out and see what happens! After reaching these conclusions it takes little time to fit in the other numbers. In the second triangle the numbers are simply double those in the first triangle. So two is put in place of one, four is in place of two, six is in place of three, etc. Will children realise this?

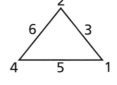

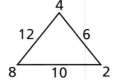

Addition triangles

In addition triangles the two numbers in each corner add to make the number in the middle. There are some missing numbers. Write these missing numbers in the circles.
Here is an example:

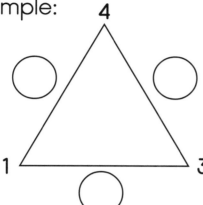

The missing numbers are:

$1 + 4 = ⑤$

$3 + 4 = ⑦$

$1 + 3 = ④$

Write these numbers in the circles.

● Complete these three addition triangles by writing in the missing numbers.

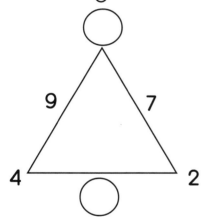 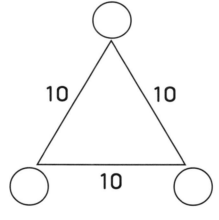 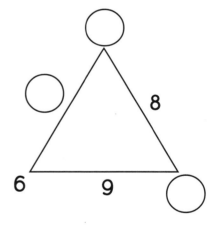

● Write the numbers given in the correct circles of these addition triangles.

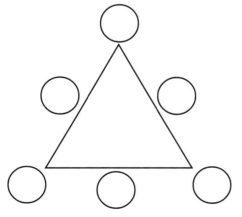 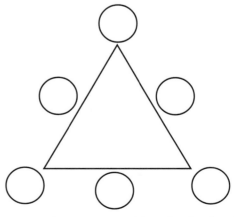

The numbers are 1, 2, 3, 4, 5, 6   The numbers are 2, 4, 6, 8, 10, 12

Mental calculation strategies and money problems

Learning objectives

◆ Develop the use of mental calculation strategies for addition and subtraction.
◆ Choose and use the appropriate number operation.
◆ Recognise each of the different values of coins.
◆ Solve word problems involving money.

Resources

AS 'Which coins?'

Teacher's notes

This problem-solving activity is about using clues to work out what coins are in a pocket.

A little logic is required.

In the first problem there are four coins. The comic is 70p but the money is not enough. It is 5p short. So the four coins must add up to 70p – 5p = 65p.
The task is then to find four coins which add up to 65p. Remember that coins can only be 1p, 2p, 5p, 10p or 20p.
The only four coins which do this are **20p + 20p + 20p + 5p** (= 65p). This is the answer.

In the second problem there are five coins. Four of these are for the same amount.
A pen for 25p can be paid for exactly with three of the coins.
The only way to get 25p from three coins is 10p + 10p + 5p = 25p.
This means that four coins must be 10p each and the other coin is 5p.
The answer is **10p + 10p + 10p + 10p + 5p = 45p**.

In the final problem there are eight coins. Four coins are the same and so are the other four. The second set of four coins have half the value of the first set. This means that the eight coins could be: four 1p and four 2p *or* four 5p and four 10p *or* four 10p and four 20p.
The next clue helps to decide which combination is correct.
The coins add up to a total which is close to £1.25.
The only combination which does this is four 10p and four 20p. These add up to £1.20.
The answer is **20p + 20p + 20p + 20p + 10p + 10p + 10p + 10p** (= £1.20).

Which coins?

Read each coin problem carefully. Then answer the questions.

The coins in these problems can only be 20p or less.

● I have four coins in my pocket. I want to buy a comic for 70p but I am 5p short. What four coins are in my pocket?

_____

● I have five coins in my pocket. Four of these coins are the same. The fifth coin is different. I decide to buy a pen costing 25p. I can pay the exact amount with three coins. How much have I in my pocket?

_____

● I have eight coins in my pocket. Four coins are the same. The other four coins are also the same but worth half the amount of the first four. I want to go to the cinema. The ticket costs £1.25 but I have not quite enough money. What coins are in my pocket?

_____

● Make up a coin problem of your own.
Ask a friend to solve it.

Understanding multiplication and division, mental calculation strategies

Learning objectives

◆ Understand operations of multiplication and division and related vocabulary.
◆ Recognise the use of symbols for unknowns.

Resources

AS 'Missing symbols'

Teacher's notes

In this activity children are presented with incomplete equations. The symbols x and ÷ are missing. These symbols have to be put in the empty circles to complete the equations.

Each of the first two equations has one missing symbol. In the first equation a division sign is missing while in the second equation it is a multiplication sign which is missing.

120 ÷ 4 = 30　and　**15 x 6 = 90**

The next four equations have two symbols missing from each of them. Each pair of equations have the same numbers but different totals.

40 x 10 ÷ 4 = 100　and　**40 ÷ 10 ÷ 4 = 1**

20 ÷ 4 x 10 = 50　and　**20 x 4 ÷ 10 = 8**

The final two equations have three symbols missing from each of them.
The answers are underlined. There are four other totals which can be obtained by various combinations of x and ÷ signs. These are also given below:

20 x 2 x 5 x 2 = 400; <u>**20 x 2 x 5 ÷ 2 = 100**</u>; 20 ÷ 2 x 5 ÷ 2 = 25;

20 x 2 ÷ 5 x 2 = 16; 20 x 2 ÷ 5 ÷ 2 = 4; <u>**20 ÷ 2 ÷ 5 ÷ 2 = 1**</u>

It is possible to get a total of 16. (20 x 2 ÷ 5 x 2 = 16).

It is not possible to get a total of 50.

Missing symbols

These number sentences can be completed by putting in a x or ÷ in each circle.

Example: 12 ◯ 5 = 60   32 ◯ 4 = 8

    Put a x sign in this circle.   Put a ÷ sign in this circle.

● Each of these number sentences has one missing symbol.

    120 ◯ 4 = 30   15 ◯ 6 = 90

● These number sentences each have two symbols missing.

40 ◯ 10 ◯ 4 = 100   40 ◯ 10 ◯ 4 = 1

20 ◯ 4 ◯ 10 = 50   20 ◯ 4 ◯ 10 = 8

● These number sentences have three missing symbols.

20 ◯ 2 ◯ 5 ◯ 2 = 1

20 ◯ 2 ◯ 5 ◯ 2 = 100

● Is it possible to make 16 from the number sentence above?

If so, write it down. _____

● Is it possible to make 50 from the number sentence above?

If so, write it down. _____

    Maths for the More Able 2

Understanding multiplication and division, mental calculation strategies

Learning objectives

◆ Understand the operations of halving and doubling.
◆ Understand that halving reverses doubling and vice versa.

Resources

AS 'Odds and evens'

Teacher's notes

In this activity children make decisions on whether a number is odd or even and either subtract one or divide a number by two. The aim is to find a number that creates the longest sequence.

For numbers between 10 and 30 the longest sequence is made by **17**.
$17 + 1 = 18$; $18 ÷ 2 = 9$; $9 + 1 = 10$; $10 ÷ 2 = 5$; $5 + 1 = 6$; $6 ÷ 2 = 3$; $3 + 1 = 4$; $4 ÷ 2 = 2$; $2 ÷ 2 = 1$

17 creates a sequence of nine steps.

19 also produces a long sequence of eight steps.

$19 + 1 = 20$; $20 ÷ 2 = 10$; $10 ÷ 2 = 5$; $5 + 1 = 6$; $6 ÷ 2 = 3$; $3 + 1 = 4$; $4 ÷ 2 = 2$; $2 ÷ 2 = 1$

Children will see that at some point in sequences the number patterns become the same. With 17 and 19 the sequences become the same when 10 is produced.
Some other numbers form a sequence with eight in it. This quickly leads to one.
The number between 10 and 30 which has the shortest sequence is **16**.

$16 ÷ 2 = 8$; $8 ÷ 2 = 4$; $4 ÷ 2 = 2$; $2 ÷ 2 = 1$

16 creates a sequence of four steps.

The reason for this short sequence is that 16 is a multiple of two and it has no other factors. Consequently, 16 simply continues to halve until one is reached. There is no step where one is added. Other numbers like eight, 32 and 64 will form the same sequences.

The number 15 starts by adding one and then has a sequence like 16. So 15 creates a short sequence of five steps. After working out a few sequences it is possible to predict how a number sequence will develop.

Initially, children may think that the larger the number then the longer the sequence. This is not so. As an example, look at 29. First one is added to make 30. Then 30 is divided by two to make 15. After one is added the sequence develops like 16. It has a total of seven steps.

Odds and evens

Pick a number between 10 and 30, for example the number **13**. Start with this chosen number and create an interesting sequence.

This is what you do: **When there is an odd number add 1 and when there is an even number divide by 2 (halve).**

$13 + 1 = 14$ $14 \div 2 = 7$ $7 + 1 = 8$ $8 \div 2 = 4$ $4 \div 2 = 2$ $2 \div 2 = 1$

The sequence stops at 1. The number of steps in the sequence is the number of equal signs. This is 6.

If the number chosen is **22**, then

$22 \div 2 = 11$ $11 + 1 = 12$ $12 \div 2 = 6$ $6 \div 2 = 3$ $3 + 1 = 4$
$4 \div 2 = 2$ $2 \div 2 = 1$

This sequence is longer than the first one. It has 7 steps in it.

● Try other numbers between 10 and 30.
● What is the longest sequence you can get? Which number creates this?

● What is the shortest sequence? Which number between 10 and 30 creates this?

Time

Learning objectives

◆ Solve simple word problems involving time.
◆ Explain how a problem was solved and which operations were selected.

Resources

AS 'Saturday'

Teacher's notes

In this decision-making activity children have to work out when a series of tasks can be carried out. The tasks must be arranged in a logical sequence. For example, it would be no good visiting a friend before getting dressed.

Certain things like watching two TV programmes and having dinner and lunch take place at specific times.

Children start by deciding on a time to get up.

This is one possible sequence:

Time	Things to do
8 o'clock	Get out of bed
8:00 – 8:30	Breakfast
8:30 – 9:00	Get washed and dressed
9:00 – 10:00	Wash and dry hair
10:00 – 11:00	Tidy bedroom
11:00 – 11:30	Housework
11:30 – 12:00	(free time)
12:00 – 12:30	Lunch
12:30 – 1:00	Watch TV
1:00 – 3:00	Shopping
3:00 – 6:00	Visit a friend
6:00 – 6:30	Dinner
6:30 – 7:00	Walk the dog
7:00 – 8:30	Watch TV
8:30 – 10:00	(free time)

Suggest to the children that if there are periods of time left unfilled then mark these in as free time.

Saturday

Teresa is planning what to do on Saturday.
- Can you help Teresa by working out what she can do and when?
- Write your list of things to do and the times of the day you would do them.

Teresa has lunch at about 12 o'clock. It takes 30 minutes.

Teresa has dinner at about 6 o'clock. It takes 30 minutes.

Teresa has to be home by 10 o'clock in the evening.

Watch two TV programmes
12.30 – 1.00 (afternoon)
and
7.00 – 8.30 (evening)

Help with some housework
30 minutes

Tidy bedroom
1 hour

Make breakfast and wash dishes – 30 minutes

Wash and dry hair
1 hour

Go shopping
2 hours

Get washed and dressed
30 minutes

Visit a friend
3 hours

Walk the dog
30 minutes

Time	Things to do
	Get out of bed

Maths for the More Able 2

Capacity

Learning objectives

◆ Solve simple 'real-life' word problems involving capacity.
◆ Understand and use the vocabulary related to capacity.
◆ Understand the relationship between units of capacity (litres and millilitres).

Resources

AS 'Fizzy drinks'

Teacher's notes

In this problem-solving activity children are working out the volume of soft drinks consumed and the amounts remaining. The activity is in two parts.

In part one children are first asked how many glasses are in each bottle.

Each bottle has a one-litre capacity and a glass has a 100ml capacity.
Each bottle can fill 10 glasses.

Three children have a mixture of drinks. In total the following have been consumed:

Four glasses of orangeade; four glasses of lemonade; four glasses of limeade.

This means that six glasses of each remain. **There are 600ml left in each bottle**.

A line is drawn on each bottle as an estimate of where the levels will be in each bottle.

In the second part two more children have drinks. The total consumed is:

Five glasses of orangeade and five glasses of lemonade.

This means that **only one glass of orangeade and one glass of lemonade are left**.

Neither Charlotte nor Peter can get the drinks they want.

Fizzy drinks

There are three bottles of fizzy drinks. Each bottle contains 1 litre.

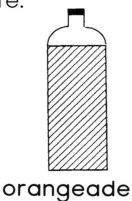
orangeade

lemonade

limeade

Each glass at a party has a capacity of 100ml.

● How many glasses can be filled from each bottle? _____

At the party three children have these drinks:
Alice has 2 glasses of lemonade and 2 glasses of orangeade.
Mark has 3 glasses of limeade and 1 glass of lemonade.
Lee has 2 glasses of orangeade, 1 glass of limeade and 1 glass of lemonade.

● What is left in each bottle?

orangeade _____ml   lemonade _____ml   limeade _____ml

● Draw a line on each bottle to show where the drink levels might be.

Two more children then have these drinks:
Anu has 2 glasses of orangeade and 3 glasses of lemonade.
Gemma has 3 glasses of orangeade and 2 glasses of lemonade.

Charlotte and Peter both want 1 glass of orangeade and 2 glasses of lemonade.

● Can Charlotte and Peter get these drinks?   Yes / No

● Explain your answer. _____

_____

Maths for the More Able 2

First published 2001 by Folens Limited.
United Kingdom: Folens Publishers, Apex Business Centre, Boscombe Road, Dunstable, LU5 4RL.
Email: folens@folens.com

Ireland: Folens Publishers, Greenhills Road, Tallaght, Dublin 24.
Email: info@folens.ie

Poland: JUKA, ul. Renesansowa 38, Warsaw 01-905

Folens allows photocopying of pages marked 'copiable page' for educational use, providing that this use is within the confines of the purchasing institution. Copiable pages should not be declared in any return in respect of any photocopying licence.

Editor: Jill Adam
Layout artist: Suzanne Ward
Illustrations: Kirsty Wilson – Graham-Cameron Illustration
Cover design: Martin Cross

© 2001 Folens Limited, on behalf of the author.

Every effort has been made to trace the copyright holders of material used in this publication. If any copyright holder has been overlooked, we should be pleased to make any necessary arrangements.

British Library Cataloguing in Publication Data. A catalogue record for this publication is available from the British Library.

ISBN 1 84163 937–0